Start Reading 2

Derek Strange

OXFORD UNIVERSITY PRESS

Friendly faces

This man is a bus-driver.

1

Hello. My name is Dave. This is my bus.

This is Tina. She is a teacher.

2

Hello. I am Tina. This is my classroom.

This is Bob. He is a policeman.

3

Hello. I am a policeman. This is my bicycle.

This woman is a nurse.

4

My name is Nancy. I am a nurse.

Pete is a pilot.

Hello. My name is Pete.

This is Dot. She is a doctor.

Hello. I am Dot.

Exercises

A True or false?

1 Dave is a bus-driver. _True_

2 Tina is a teacher. _____

3 Pete is a doctor. _____

4 Nancy is a pilot. _____

5 Bob is a policeman. _____

6 Dot is a nurse. _____

B Write She or He .

1 BOB ___He___ is a policeman.

2 NANCY _____ is a nurse.

3 DAVE _____ is a bus-driver.

4 TINA _____ is a teacher.

5 DOT _____ is a doctor.

6 PETE _____ is a pilot.

C Write the words in the squares.

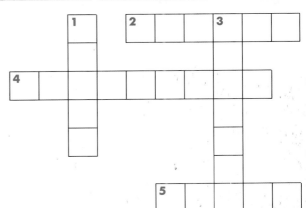

Mr. Fingers

Exercises

A Answer the questions.

1 Is he a magician? _Yes, he is._

2 Is this a hat? _____

3 Is this a duck? _____

4 Is she a magician? _____

5 Is this an orange? _____

6 Is this Mr. Fingers? _____

B What is this? Write sentences.

1 _It is an orange._

2 _____

3 _____

4 _____

5 _____

6 _____

5

A naughty dog

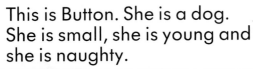

This is Button. She is a dog. She is small, she is young and she is naughty.

The door is open . . .

1

A bowl . . . Mmm. What is it?
It is soft and it is cold . . .
It is ice-cream!
Green and yellow ice-cream.

2

And a cake.
A big brown cake on a plate.

3

Mmm. I am happy now.

4

Oh no! The table-cloth!

5

What is this? . . .
Oh no! It is Button.

6

6

Exercises

A True or false?

1 Button is young. _____
2 The ice-cream is yellow
  and brown. _____
3 The cake is yellow. _____
4 The ice-cream is cold. _____
5 Button is naughty. _____

B Finish the words.

1 C ___ ___ D
2 ___ ___ L ___ O W
3 ___ ___ O W ___
4 Y ___ U ___ G
5 N ___ ___ ___ H ___ Y

C Match the sentences with the pictures.

1 This dog is clean.

2 This dog is dirty.

3 This dog is happy.

4 This dog is fat.

5 This dog is unhappy.

6 This dog is naughty.

The red bag

Exercises

A Read and match.

1 Mr. Z is holding up . . .

2 The woman is writing . . .

3 The man is standing . . .

4 The man is speaking . . .

5 Mr. Z is pointing . . .

6 The woman is running . . .

. . . at the bag.

. . . to a bus.

. . . near his car.

. . . in a small book.

. . . to the woman.

. . . his hand.

B Make sentences.

1 is | to | telephone | The | walking | . | man | the

2 A | standing | woman | . | there | is

3 woman | . | The | smiling | is

4 at | her | is | He | bag | . | pointing

5 to | She | running | a | . | is | bus

C Write the words in the squares.

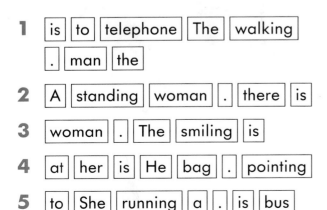

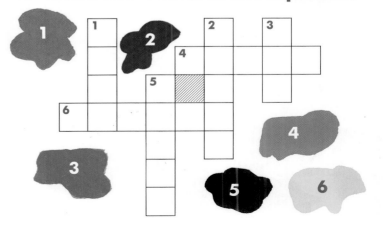

'SKY BIRD'

1 This is the spaceship 'SKY BIRD'.

This is one room in the spaceship. It is very small. Look at the black and red buttons on the wall and on the ceiling. The buttons are in front of the astronaut's seat. They are near the astronaut's hands.

3 The seat is in the middle of the room. The radio is beside the astronaut's head. And a lamp is beside the radio.

Beside the seat, on the floor, are four small green cupboards. The astronaut's books and pens and rulers are in the cupboards.

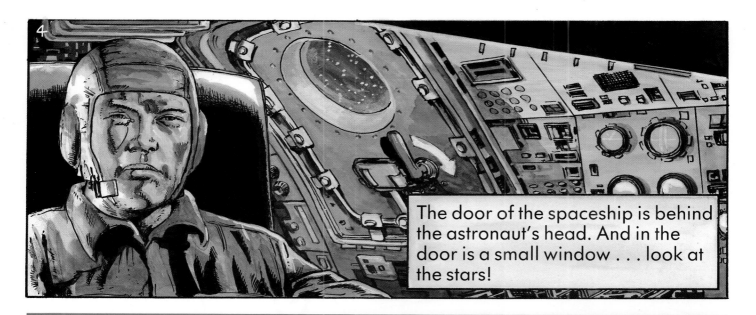

The door of the spaceship is behind the astronaut's head. And in the door is a small window . . . look at the stars!

Exercises

A Read and match.

1 The black and red buttons are on . . .
2 The buttons are . . .
3 The astronaut's seat is . . .
4 The radio is . . .
5 The four small green cupboards are . . .

. . . in the middle of the room.
. . . in front of the astronaut's seat.
. . . on the floor, beside the seat.
. . . the wall and on the ceiling.
. . . beside the astronaut's head.

B Make words.

1 odari = _____
2 stubnot = _____
3 pudrascob = _____
4 glinice = _____
5 otarastun = _____

C Look at the picture. Finish the sentences.

| beside | in front of | middle | on | behind |

1 The seat is in the _____ of the room.
2 The box is _____ the seat, on the floor.
3 The radio is _____ the seat, on the floor.
4 The cupboard is _____ the seat, near the door.
5 The lamp is _____ the wall, near the cupboard.

The secret room

Exercises

A True or false?

1 There is a key in one door of the old house. _____
2 There are tables and chairs in the big room. _____
3 There is a secret room behind one of the walls. _____
4 There is an old radio in the secret room. _____

B Write **There is** or **There are** .

1 _____ _____ an old house near the river.
2 _____ _____ two doors at the front of the house.
3 _____ _____ stairs at the back of the big room.
4 _____ _____ a small button in the middle of one wall.
5 _____ _____ not a lamp in the secret room.

C Answer the questions: **Yes, there is** or **No, there is not** .
Yes, there are or **No, there are not** .

1 Is there a pencil on your desk now? _____
2 Are there cars in the street now? _____
3 Is there a bird in the sky now? _____
4 Are there books in your bag now? _____
5 Is there a cupboard in your classroom? _____

Alphabets

What are these?

तुम और बच्चा

με θαύριο

Что это?
Это спутник

أحمد علي

Veni, vidi, vici

Good morning!

They are letters of different alphabets.

What are letters?

Letters are lines ═══ |||||||| ////////// \\\\\\\\\

and dots • • • •• • ●● ¨ ...

and crosses. ✝ ✝ ✝✝ ✝ ✝✝ ✝ ✕✕✕✕✕

I am writing these words with letters and you are reading my words.

How many different alphabets are there?

There are fifty or sixty different alphabets.
Five of these are the main alphabets. I am writing these words in the Roman alphabet.
There are twenty-six letters in the Roman alphabet.

a b c d e f g
h i j k l m n o p
q r s t u v w x
y z

The Roman alphabet

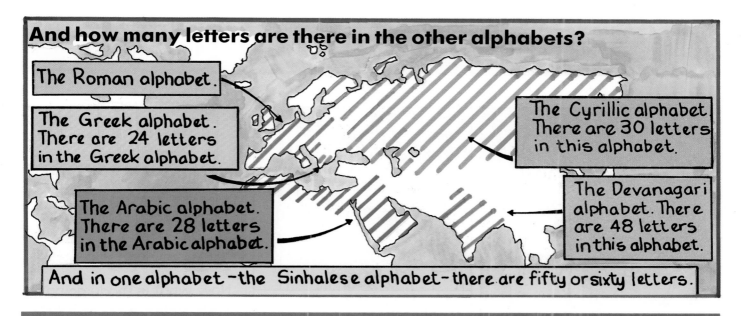

And how many letters are there in the other alphabets?

The Roman alphabet.

The Greek alphabet. There are 24 letters in the Greek alphabet.

The Arabic alphabet. There are 28 letters in the Arabic alphabet.

The Cyrillic alphabet. There are 30 letters in this alphabet.

The Devanagari alphabet. There are 48 letters in this alphabet.

And in one alphabet – the Sinhalese alphabet – there are fifty or sixty letters.

Exercises

A Make sentences.

1 are │ or │ . │ There │ alphabets │ different │ sixty │ fifty

2 writing │ letters │ I │ words │ these │ . │ with │ am

3 ? │ many │ there │ How │ are │ different │ alphabets

4 . │ are │ the │ alphabet │ letters │ 48 │ in │ Devanagari │ There

5 letters │ There │ . │ in │ are │ Arabic │ 28 │ alphabet │ the

B Read and match.

1 Ten and five is . . .
2 Fifteen and twenty-five is . . .
3 Fifty and twenty is . . .
4 Sixty and thirty is . . .
5 Seventy and fifteen is . . .

. . . forty.
. . . eighty-five.
. . . ninety.
. . . fifteen.
. . . seventy.

$10 + 5 = ?$

$15 + 25 = ?$

$50 + 20 = ?$

$60 + 30 = ?$

$70 + 15 = ?$

C Answer the questions.

1 How many dots are there?
2 How many crosses are there?
3 How many lines are there?
4 How many stairs are there?
5 How many letters are there in this word?

Mrs. Parker's floor

Paddy is a painter. Today he is working at Mrs. Parker's house. Mrs. Parker is an old woman.

Mrs. Parker is speaking to Paddy. She is pointing at an old cupboard. Paddy is listening.

Now what is Paddy doing? He is wearing dirty trousers and an old shirt. He is carrying a pot of paint in his hand.

He is pushing the cupboard into the middle of the floor. Mrs. Parker is putting a newspaper on the floor, under the cupboard.

Paddy is painting the cupboard. He is singing a song. He is happy.

What is he doing now? He is not painting the cupboard.

He is drinking a cup of coffee and he is reading the newspaper.

Now he is painting again...but where is the newspaper? It is not on the floor. Stop, Paddy! He is painting the floor. Stop!

Mrs. Parker is looking at the floor. She is not happy.

Paddy is washing the floor. Mrs. Parker is happy now.

Exercises

A True or false?

1 (Picture 2) There is an old cupboard in Mrs. Parker's house. _____
2 (Picture 4) Paddy is putting a newspaper on the floor. _____
3 (Picture 5) Mrs. Parker is painting the old cupboard. _____
4 (Picture 5) Paddy is singing a song. _____
5 (Picture 6) Paddy is reading the newspaper. _____

B Answer the questions.

1 (Picture 1) Where is Paddy today?
2 (Picture 2) Who is speaking to Paddy?
3 (Picture 3) What is Paddy wearing?
4 (Picture 4) What is Mrs. Parker doing in this picture?
5 (Picture 7) What is Paddy doing in this picture?

C Make words.

1 forlo = _____
2 tranipe = _____
3 sortruse = _____
4 pransweep = _____
5 focefe = _____

A picnic story

1

Jack and Alex are going to the river for a picnic. There are sandwiches, cakes, bananas and pears in the basket . . . and Jack has a big bottle of Pepsi. Alex has two towels in his bag – they are going swimming.

2

They have good bicycles. They are riding beside the river now. Jack has the picnic basket on the back of his bicycle.

3

They are under a big tree near the river. The picnic basket is beside the tree. Alex is taking the towels from his bag. A cow is looking at Alex and Jack.

4

They are swimming in the river. The cow is looking at the basket. She is smelling the cakes and sandwiches. She is hungry.

5

Oh no! The cow has a pear in her mouth – she is eating the picnic!

6

Now the children are looking at the cow. They are shouting, but the cow is not listening. She is eating.

7

Jack has a stick — he is throwing the stick at the cow and Alex is shouting. But the cow is not hungry now . . . and there are no sandwiches or cakes for the children.

Exercises

A Answer the questions.

1   What is his name?

2   And what is his friend's name?

3 (Picture 2)
   Where are the children going?

4 (Picture 5)
   What is the cow eating?

5 (Picture 7)
   What is Jack throwing at the cow?

B Write have or has .

1 The children _____ a picnic basket.
2 Jack _____ a big bottle in his hand.
3 Alex _____ two towels in his bag.
4 Alex and Jack _____ good bicycles.
5 The cow _____ a pear in her mouth.

C Write the words in the squares.

Across (→)

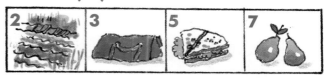

Down (↓)

19

Going fishing

Wednesday Ten o'clock.

I am on holiday on Sea Island. The sun is shining and it is hot.

My friend Lesley is here with her father. They have a small boat. We are going fishing.

Sea Island.

Five o'clock in the afternoon.

There are big, black clouds in the sky and it is raining. The wind is pushing us out to sea...

Eight o'clock.

It is not raining now. It is night and the moon is in the sky. The wind is pushing the boat out, out, out to sea. We have no supper and we are very hungry. We have some coffee, but we are cold and unhappy.

Eleven o'clock.

Lesley is sleeping now.   There is a ship out there, but we have no lamp.

Thursday morning.

It is seven o'clock in the morning. The sun is shining again. There is a small island and there are men and women near the boats. Lesley is waving her handkerchief and her father is shouting...

Half past seven.
Two of the boats are coming out from the island! We are OK!

Friday.
We are with Lesley's mother on Sea Island again. She is very happy to see us.

Exercises

A True or false?

1 It is raining on Thursday morning. _____

2 At five o'clock on Wednesday afternoon there are black clouds in the sky. _____

3 The man and the children have no supper, but they have some coffee. _____

4 On Thursday morning they are near a small island. _____

B Read and match.

1 It is eight o'clock.

2 It is eleven o'clock.

3 It is five o'clock.

4 It is half past seven.

5 It is half past three.

C Make sentences.

1 | clouds | sky | . | are | There | black | the | in | big |

2 | boat | . | The | pushing | to | is | the | sea | out | wind |

3 | It | o'clock | in | . | seven | morning | the | is |

4 | and | small | Lesley | her | a | father | . | have | boat |

5 | very | and | We | cold | . | hungry | are |

21

Picture dictionary

 a banana

 a basket

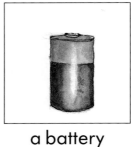 a battery

 a bicycle

 big   small

 a boat

 a bottle

 a bowl

 a boy a girl a man a woman

 a bus

 a bus-driver

 a button

 a classroom

 a cloud

  coffee

 a cow

 a cupboard

 a doctor

 a door

 drinking

  drinking

 a duck

 fishing

 green

 hair

a handkerchief   a hat   a hen   hot   a key

a lamp   a magician   a newspaper   a nurse   old   young

open   closed   paint   a painter   a pear

a pilot   a plate   a pot   a radio   reading

a river   a ceiling   a wall   a floor   a room   a ruler   a sandwich

a seat

a shirt

shouting

smelling

smiling

stairs

a stick

supper

a table-cloth

thin

throwing

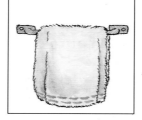
a towel

a town

trousers

walking

wind

day   night

behind   in front of   beside

near   on   under

across   in the middle of   down

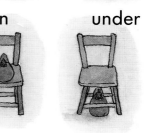